Contents

Note for parents, tutors, teachers and other adult helpers
A pull-out answers section (pages A1 to A8) appears in the centre of this book, between pages 26 and 27 (Paper 10). This provides answers to all the questions, along with guidance on marking the papers. Remove the pull-out section before the child begins working through the practice papers.

Verbal Reasoning Progress Paper 7

MARK
✓ OR ✗

Q. 1–5

spot the word

A four-letter word is hidden in each of these sentences. You will find the hidden word at the end of one word and the beginning of the next. Underline the hidden word and then write it on the line.

Example Daniel <u>end</u>ed his speech with a joke. ___lend___

1   David might ask his mum if he can go to the cinema. _____   1 ☐

2   The free footballs were offered to all children in the school.
_____   2 ☐

3   The bad weather each day kept people indoors. _____   3 ☐

4   Rashid asked why the sun didn't shine at night. _____   4 ☐

5   Each elephant was given a name by the children. _____   5 ☐

Q. 6–10

letter sequences

Write the next two items in each sequence. Use the alphabet to help you.

Example AB   CD   EF   GH   __IJ__   __KL__

A B C D E F G H I J K L M N O P Q R S T U V W X Y Z

6   B   D   F   H   J   _____ _____   6 ☐

7   Z   X   V   T   R   _____ _____   7 ☐

8   J   L   N   P   R   _____ _____   8 ☐

9   BC   FG   JK   NO   RS   _____ _____   9 ☐

10   TS   QP   NM   KJ   HG   _____ _____   10 ☐

Q. 11–15

mixed-up sentences

Two words must swap places for each sentence to make sense. Underline these **two** words in each sentence.

Example The <u>bone</u> growled softly as he approached the <u>dog</u>.

11   The potatoes dug up the gardener in the allotment.   11 ☐

12   She think I has gone to live with her relations in Cornwall.   12 ☐

13   Harry was upset when he lost his shopping in the mobile centre.   13 ☐

14   The teacher was asleep when I fell angry at my desk.   14 ☐

15   We had not happy when we saw the damage that were been caused.   15 ☐

MARK ☐

MARK
✓ OR ✗

Q. 16–20 word connections	Underline the **one** word from the brackets that fits best with the three words at the start. **Example** feed eat scoff (hate mock laugh false <u>devour</u>)	
	16 sling throw fling (bandage arm chuck drop shot)	**16** ☐
	17 hail snow sleet (weather sunny rain wellingtons cloud)	**17** ☐
	18 scheme plot proposal (engagement plan pilot bonfire deed)	**18** ☐
	19 pretty appealing attractive (ugly magnet hurt friendly handsome)	**19** ☐
	20 accurate concise correct (incise precise excise exercise wrong)	**20** ☐

Q. 21–25 number sequences	Write the next two numbers in each sequence. **Example** 2 4 6 8 <u>10</u> <u>12</u>	
	21 7 13 19 25 _____ _____	**21** ☐
	22 15 16 18 21 _____ _____	**22** ☐
	23 36 31 26 21 _____ _____	**23** ☐
	24 $2\frac{3}{4}$ $3\frac{1}{2}$ $4\frac{1}{4}$ 5 _____ _____	**24** ☐
	25 6 12 18 24 _____ _____	**25** ☐

Q. 26–30 analogies	Underline **one** word to complete these analogies. **Example** Arrive is to depart as come is to (run hurry <u>go</u> hide).	
	26 September is to July as March is to (hare January wind month May).	**26** ☐
	27 Two is to bicycle as three is to (unicycle wheel transport tricycle pedal).	**27** ☐
	28 Train is to rails as barge is to (horse canal road transport passenger).	**28** ☐
	29 Dog is to puppy as human is to (relative son baby daughter nephew).	**29** ☐
	30 Whale is to pod as (class family fish country teacher) is to staff.	**30** ☐

MARK ☐

MARK
✓ OR ✗

Q. 31–35

word categories

Below this table are 10 words. Write each word in the correct column.

31 money	32 animals	33 trees	34 food	35 liquids

lemonade   cent   ash   euro   spaghetti   terrapin
birch   platypus   cereal   water

31 ☐
32 ☐
33 ☐
34 ☐
35 ☐

Q. 36–40

missing letters

The same letter will end the first word and begin the next word. Write the letter.

Example PAN (T) URN

36 STAR (__) EASE

37 BORE (__) RAIN

38 PLEA (__) REAM

39 SPIN (__) ASTER

40 LATE (__) AMBLE

36 ☐
37 ☐
38 ☐
39 ☐
40 ☐

Q. 41–45

synonyms

Underline two words, **one** from **each** set of brackets, that are **similar** in meaning.

Example (large great tiny huge) (box small hungry crate)

41 (gigantic tunnel small beans)   (nasty vast wide narrow)

42 (penny wise stupid empty)   (full sensible brief false)

43 (flower silly upset angry)   (vase afraid enraged disgusted)

44 (fearless lucky fright cowardly)   (scarred unfortunate temper brave)

45 (different maybe ugly identical)   (near same almost nearly)

41 ☐
42 ☐
43 ☐
44 ☐
45 ☐

MARK ☐

MARK
✓ OR ✗

Q. 46–50 symbol codes	The word **STEAL** is written as **13759** in code. Use the same code to find the hidden words.

46 13597 _____ 46 ☐

47 37591 _____ 47 ☐

48 19537 _____ 48 ☐

49 97513 _____ 49 ☐

50 35971 _____ 50 ☐

Q. 51–55
make a word

Look at how the second word is made from the first word in each pair. Complete the third pair in the same way. Write the answers on the lines.

Example (fright rights) (flight lights) (height _eights_)

51 (sty sties)   (fly flies)   (try _____) 51 ☐

52 (stun nuts)   (spat taps)   (rats _____) 52 ☐

53 (fuse refused)   (pose reposed)   (tire _____) 53 ☐

54 (breath bath)   (arable able)   (stream _____) 54 ☐

55 (leopard leap)   (beaters beet)   (plagues _____) 55 ☐

Q. 56–60
word chains

Turn the word on the left into the word on the right. You can only change one letter at a time. Each change must result in a real word.

Example TALE _TAKE_   _LAKE_   LIKE

56 P L A Y _____ _____ S L I P 56 ☐

57 T R A M _____ _____ P L A Y 57 ☐

58 T Y P E _____ _____ S O R E 58 ☐

59 M A L E _____ _____ D O M E 59 ☐

60 T E L L _____ _____ M A L E 60 ☐

MARK ☐

MARK
✓ OR ✗

Q. 61–65

always has

Look at the word in **bold**. Underline **one** option in the brackets. It must describe what the word in bold **always has**.

Example A **lake** always has (boats <u>water</u> ducks swimmers fish).

61 A **fish** always has (water a pond food gills chips bait).   61 ☐

62 A **bicycle** always has (a bell a basket a frame a rider a lamp).   62 ☐

63 A **quadruped** always has (fur feet a kennel a bark walks).   63 ☐

64 **Soup** is always (hot tasty wet tomato spicy lumpy).   64 ☐

65 A **house** always has (a cellar walls a chimney an attic taps).   65 ☐

Q. 66–70

missing
three-letter
words

In each of these sentences, the word in CAPITALS has three letters missing. These three letters make a real three-letter word. Write the three-letter word on the line.

Example My father SED me a photo of my mother.   <u>HOW</u>

66 I ran across the road and was NLY run over.   _____   66 ☐

67 We went to the THRE to see a pantomime.   _____   67 ☐

68 There was an AWKD silence when Millie said she wasn't going.

   _____   68 ☐

69 Many people take up GARING as an outdoor hobby.   _____   69 ☐

70 Italy is on the CONENT of Europe.   _____   70 ☐

Q. 71–75

letters for
numbers

If **A** is **2**, **B** is **3**, **C** is **5**, **D** is **10** and **E** is **12**, work out these calculations. Give the answer as a letter.

Example $A + B = \blacksquare$ <u>C</u>

71 $A \times B \times D \div E = \blacksquare$ _____   71 ☐

72 $(E \div B) \times C = 2 \times \blacksquare$ _____   72 ☐

73 $B \times C \times A = \blacksquare \times 3$ _____   73 ☐

74 $(E + B + C) \div A = \blacksquare$ _____   74 ☐

75 $D - (C \times A) + \blacksquare = 12$ _____   75 ☐

MARK ☐

MARK
✓ OR ✗

Q. 76–80

odd ones out

One word in each question does **not** belong with the rest. Underline this word.

Example horrid   nasty   <u>kind</u>   mean   unfriendly

76	cure	remedy	solution	disease	healing	repair	76
77	unclean	dirty	mucky	foul	tarnished	spotless	77
78	answer	mystery	enigma	puzzle	riddle	conundrum	78
79	hasten	rush	dally	hurry	race	scurry	79
80	rosemary	sage	mint	thyme	broccoli	parsley	80

Q. 81–85

jumbled words with clues

Each question has a word in CAPITALS. The letters in this word have been mixed up. Use the clue to work out what the word is. Write it on the line.

Example NIBOR   (a bird)   <u>ROBIN</u>

81	LBATE (the noise made by a lamb)	_____	81
82	LBATSE (where a horse lives)	_____	82
83	LBETSEE (insects)	_____	83
84	POPHI (a very large animal)	_____	84
85	ERLALGY (a building where art is displayed)	_____	85

Q. 86–90

which word

One word in each question **cannot** be made from the word in CAPITALS. Underline this word. You may only use each letter once.

Example AIRPORT   rip   <u>park</u>   trio   pair   roar

86	TRAIPSE	part	strap	stripe	seat	spate	spares	86
87	CARRIAGE	cage	eager	rage	gear	carer	crag	87
88	REGIMENT	grime	integer	green	mentor	tree	miner	88
89	PERSONAL	parson	leapt	reason	leaps	prone	slope	89
90	ENTITLES	sleet	tiles	intent	steel	stint	lest	90

MARK

MARK
✓ OR ✗

Q. 91–95

word grids

Fit each set of words into the grid. The words should read across and down.

91

e	a	r

bee   oak   eke
boa   ~~ear~~   are

91 ☐

92

b	a	y

ray   bye   ~~bay~~
rye   ebb   err

92 ☐

93

n	o	r

try   toy   coo
ant   ~~nor~~   act

93 ☐

94

n	o	d

doe   ego   ~~nod~~
goo   ode   end

94 ☐

95

d	u	e

den   art   rue
~~due~~   ten   add

95 ☐

MARK ☐

MARK
✓ OR ✗

Q. 96–100

compound words

Write **one** word that can be written **in front** of each of the words in the question to make a longer compound word.

Example work side man guard wood   _fire_

96	agent	paper	caster	reader	flash	_____	96 ☐
97	age	man	code	card	master	_____	97 ☐
98	thing	body	what	where	time	_____	98 ☐
99	bag	some	brake	shake	saw	_____	99 ☐
100	row	man	rack	on	gain	_____	100 ☐

MARK ☐

END OF TEST

PROGRESS PAPER 7 TOTAL ☐

Q. 1–5

interpreting graphs

This graph shows the percentage of children who passed their English exam between 2009 and 2013. Circle the correct answers.

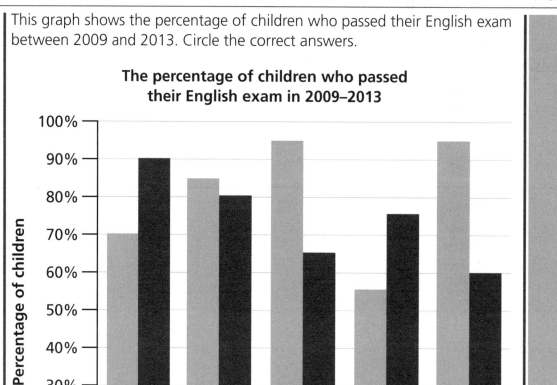

The percentage of children who passed their English exam in 2009–2013

1 In which years did the same percentage of girls pass the exam?

2009   2010   2011   2012   2013

2 In which year did 10% fewer boys pass the exam than the year before?

2009   2010   2011   2012   2013

3 In which two years did the boys achieve their best results?

2009   2010   2011   2012   2013

4 Which year produced the greatest difference between boys and girls?

2009   2010   2011   2012   2013

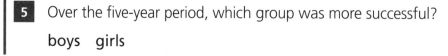

5 Over the five-year period, which group was more successful?

boys   girls

1 ☐

2 ☐

3 ☐

4 ☐

5 ☐

MARK ☐

MARK
✓ OR ✗

Q. 6–10

alphabetical order

Number the words in each line in alphabetical order. Use the alphabet to help you.

Example

CAT	CAN	CAR	CAW	CAB	CAP
5	2	4	6	1	3

A B C D E F G H I J K L M N O P Q R S T U V W X Y Z

6 BAT ☐   BAN ☐   BAD ☐   BAY ☐   BAR ☐   BAG ☐   6 ☐

7 PAVE ☐   PATE ☐   PARE ☐   PACE ☐   PANE ☐   PAGE ☐   7 ☐

8 SINGLE ☐   SINGER ☐   SINGE ☐   SING ☐   SINGLET ☐   SINGING ☐   8 ☐

9 SLEIGH ☐   SLOUGH ☐   SIGH ☐   SLIGHT ☐   SIGHT ☐   COUGH ☐   9 ☐

10 THIGH ☐   THENCE ☐   THOUGH ☐   THERE ☐   THEIR ☐   THROUGH ☐   10 ☐

Q. 11–15

compound words

Write **one** word that can be written **in front** of the words in the question to make a longer compound word.

Example work side man guard wood ___fire___

11 rise   day   tan   burn   set   _____   11 ☐

12 set   time   bag   leaf   cup   _____   12 ☐

13 man   mate   bench   shy   top   _____   13 ☐

14 port   pet   ton   go   rot   _____   14 ☐

15 fall   break   mill   shield   swept   _____   15 ☐

Q. 16–20

mixed-up groups

Two groups of three words have been mixed up in each question. Work out which would be the **middle** word in each group if they were in the correct order. Underline these **two** words.

Example city <u>adolescent</u> village <u>town</u> infant adult

16 hut   eleven   mansion   seven   nine   house   16 ☐

17 allotment   cruiser   battleship   park   canoe   window-box   17 ☐

18 sprint   octagon   hexagon   walk   run   pentagon   18 ☐

19 gram   centimetre   millimetre   kilogram   metre   milligram   19 ☐

20 meal   cat   squirrel   sandwich   tiger   feast   20 ☐

MARK ☐

MARK
✓ OR ✗

Q. 21–25

spot the word

A four-letter word is hidden in each of these sentences. You will find the hidden word at the end of one word and the beginning of the next. Underline the hidden word and then write it on the line.

Example Daniel <u>ended</u> his speech with a joke. <u>lend</u>

21 When I cut my finger my sister put a plaster on it. _____ 21 ☐

22 You will lose your friends if you cheat at games. _____ 22 ☐

23 You will be happy to know that pizza is on the menu. _____ 23 ☐

24 The sales assistant wore a badge on his lapel. _____ 24 ☐

25 You must taste Stephen's delicious apple tart. _____ 25 ☐

Q. 26–30

add a letter

Read the clue in brackets. Add **one** letter to the word in CAPITALS to make a new word that matches the clue. Write the new word on the line.

Example CANE   (lifts heavy items)   <u>CRANE</u>

26 CRAM   (the top of the milk) _____ 26 ☐

27 HID   (an animal's skin) _____ 27 ☐

28 BEAD   (made from flour) _____ 28 ☐

29 BEAD   (hair on a man) _____ 29 ☐

30 BOWL   (part of the body) _____ 30 ☐

Q. 31–35

symbol codes

The word **IMPERTINENT** is written as £ © @ # % & £ $ # $ & in code. Use the same code to find the hidden words.

31 & % £ © _____ 31 ☐

32 % £ & # _____ 32 ☐

33 @ £ # % _____ 33 ☐

34 © £ $ & _____ 34 ☐

35 & # © @ # % _____ 35 ☐

MARK ☐

MARK
✓ OR ✗

Q. 36–40
word categories

Below this table are 15 words. Write each word in the correct column.

36 orange	37 plumber	38 potato	39 green	40 pen

mango   eraser   swede   cobbler   scarlet   apple   ruler   plum   staple
carpenter   tiler   sprout   cabbage   cerise   purple

36 ☐
37 ☐
38 ☐
39 ☐
40 ☐

Q. 41–45
word connections

Underline the **one** word that fits with **both** pairs of words in brackets.

Example (heart club) (ruby emerald)   jewel brain <u>diamond</u> card brooch

41 (wood timber) (record diary)   log remember write book carve   41 ☐

42 (cup bowl) (ship cruiser)   kayak game boat vessel liquid   42 ☐

43 (eggs chickens) (seize grasp)   hen brood grab hold clutch   43 ☐

44 (stake pole) (letters mail)   alphabet gamble post pillar job   44 ☐

45 (hide disguise) (coat cape)   find cloak lose jumper hat   45 ☐

Q. 46–50
position problems

This is a diagram of a five-storey block of flats. Five people live here. Read the information. Then work out on which floor each person lives. Write the names on the correct floor in the diagram.

Arfan, Ben, Carrie, Daniel and Elle occupy the five floors of a block of flats. Carrie lives one floor above Elle and two floors above Ben. Ben lives one floor below Elle. Arfan lives four floors below Daniel. Elle lives below Carrie but above Arfan.

Floor	Name
46 Fourth floor	
47 Third floor	
48 Second floor	
49 First floor	
50 Ground floor	

46 ☐
47 ☐
48 ☐
49 ☐
50 ☐

MARK ☐

MARK
✓ OR ✗

Q. 51–55 which word	**Two** words in each question **cannot** be made from the word in CAPITALS. Underline these words. You may only use each letter once.	
	Example AIRPORT rip <u>park</u> trio pair <u>portal</u> roar	
	51 CORPORATION port root prone poor ration carpet	51 ☐
	52 PERPETRATE peter traitor prepare trapper treat parent	52 ☐
	53 CERTIFIED defer field fried trice dirtied recited	53 ☐
	54 FASCINATED defence canted fasted antics centre fined	54 ☐
	55 OPINIONATED pined nation depend denoted pointed neon	55 ☐

Q. 56–60 analogies	Underline **one** word in **each** set of brackets to complete these analogies.	
	Example Arrive is to (<u>depart</u> plane speed) as come is to (run hurry <u>go</u>).	
	56 Hunter is to (dog gun prey) as cat is to (dog teeth mouse).	56 ☐
	57 Story is to (read author excitement) as poem is to (poet stanza rhyme).	57 ☐
	58 Frog is to (tadpole pond toad) as butterfly is to (leaf caterpillar cocoon).	58 ☐
	59 Gun is to (artillery bullet soldier) as bow is to (archery bend arrow).	59 ☐
	60 Difficult is to (complicated arduous easy) as calm is to (sea anxious safe).	60 ☐

Q. 61–65 move a letter	Take **one** letter from the first word and put it in the second word to make two new words. Write the two new words on the lines.	
	Example LIME and ZOO become <u>LIE</u> and <u>ZOOM</u>.	
	61 BRUSH and LAD become _____ and _____.	61 ☐
	62 BOUND and BOY become _____ and _____.	62 ☐
	63 BOARD and HELL become _____ and _____.	63 ☐
	64 POUND and COLD become _____ and _____.	64 ☐
	65 BABY and PLUM become _____ and _____.	65 ☐

MARK ☐

MARK
✓ OR ✗

Q. 66–70	Write the next two items in each sequence. Use the alphabet to help you.	
letter sequences	**Example** AB CD EF GH <u>IJ</u> <u>KL</u>	

A B C D E F G H I J K L M N O P Q R S T U V W X Y Z

66	SE TH UK VN WQ _____ _____	66 ☐
67	BC YX DE WV FG UT _____ _____	67 ☐
68	CF GJ KN OR SV _____ _____	68 ☐
69	XN ZQ BT DW FZ HC _____ _____	69 ☐
70	ZML UON PQP KSR FUT _____ _____	70 ☐

Q. 71–75	In each of these sentences, the word in CAPITALS has three letters missing. These three letters make a real three-letter word. Write the three-letter word on the line.	
missing three-letter words	**Example** My father SED me a photo of my mother. <u>HOW</u>	
71	The pilot skilfully LED the helicopter on the ship. _____	71 ☐
72	Swimming and dancing are my FAVITE hobbies. _____	72 ☐
73	On a clear night I can see thousands of SS. _____	73 ☐
74	That champion weight lifter is TREDOUSLY strong. _____	74 ☐
75	The OPTION on my broken ankle was successful. _____	75 ☐

Q. 76–80	Two words in each question do **not** belong with the rest. Underline these **two** words.	
odd ones out	**Example** horrid nasty <u>kind</u> mean unfriendly <u>helpful</u>	
76	sour bitter tart sweet vinegary sugary sharp	76 ☐
77	gruesome beautiful pretty dreadful hideous grim	77 ☐
78	dodge escape imprison depart flee incarcerate	78 ☐
79	wise preposterous absurd sensible ridiculous asinine	79 ☐
80	significant vital pressing memorable trivial paltry	80 ☐

MARK ☐

MARK
✓ OR ✗

Q. 81–85

complete the sentence

Underline **one** word in **each** set of brackets to make the sentence sensible.

Example The (plumber <u>electrician</u> baker) repaired the (<u>light</u> loaf sink) so that we could (lamp hear <u>see</u>) again.

81 (Do Don't Please) drop (feelings cake litter) in the (oven street chair). — 81 ☐

82 The (pupils dogs soldiers) carried the (efforts teabags books) into the (palace bathroom library). — 82 ☐

83 My (feet hands eyes) had (gloves wheat corns) so (they you I) went to see the chiropodist. — 83 ☐

84 The (cat bottle baby) (skipped shouted purred) as it (threw lapped chewed) the milk. — 84 ☐

85 The (pilot grocer barber) cut my (grass hair nails) so I would look (hungry afraid smart) for the photograph. — 85 ☐

Q. 86–90

interpreting tables

Study this table of bus fares. All the fares are shown in pence.

Answer the questions.

Valley Road							
90	Prince's Road						
105	90	Grange Street					
120	105	90	Farm Street				
140	120	105	90	Oak Avenue			
180	140	120	105	90	March Road		
195	180	140	120	105	90	Temple Road	
225	195	180	140	120	105	90	Bus Station

86 How much is the fare between Prince's Road and Oak Avenue?

_____p — 86 ☐

87 What is the fare between Farm Street and the Bus Station? _____p — 87 ☐

88 What is the fare between Valley Road and March Road? _____p — 88 ☐

89 How much is the fare for the whole journey? _____p — 89 ☐

90 What is the minimum fare? _____p — 90 ☐

MARK ☐

MARK
✓ OR ✗

Q. 91–95 synonyms	Underline two words, **one** from **each** set of brackets, that are **similar** in meaning.	
	Example (large great <u>tiny</u> huge) (box <u>small</u> hungry crate)	
91	(meadow countryside city garden) (climate farm field trees)	91 ☐
92	(household spotless filthy carpet) (dirty vacuum dust broom)	92 ☐
93	(nurse guard lamp doctor) (guide bulb imprison warder)	93 ☐
94	(property firm house shop) (business canteen bed greengrocer)	94 ☐
95	(courage bravery disguise coward) (empty mouse here mask)	95 ☐

Q. 96–100 jumbled words in sentences	The letters of the words in CAPITALS have been mixed up. Write the **two** correct words on the lines.	
	Example The TERWA was too cold to WSIM in. <u>WATER</u> and <u>SWIM</u>	
96	There are sixty NITUMES in an RHUO.	
	_____ and _____	96 ☐
97	TOLLBOFA and NESTIN are my favourite sports.	
	_____ and _____	97 ☐
98	My MECUPORT screen is broken and needs to be REERPAID.	
	_____ and _____	98 ☐
99	We are going on ALOYHID to ANIPS in August.	
	_____ and _____	99 ☐
100	The clever CETEVITED used the clues to solve the ETYSMYR.	
	_____ and _____	100 ☐

MARK ☐

END OF TEST

PROGRESS PAPER 8 TOTAL ☐

START HERE

MARK
✓ OR ✗

Q. 1–5
jumbled words with clues

Each question has a word in CAPITALS. The letters in this word have been mixed up. Use the clue to work out what the word is. Write it on the line.

Example NIBOR (a bird) __ROBIN__

1 RAIL (an animal's home) _____ 1 ☐

2 TEESET (something to sit on) _____ 2 ☐

3 RATINLEG (a geometrical shape) _____ 3 ☐

4 BOWARDER (furniture) _____ 4 ☐

5 FAKERSTAB (a meal) _____ 5 ☐

Q. 6–10
antonyms

Underline two words, **one** from **each** set of brackets, that have the **opposite** meaning.

Example (<u>happy</u> kind mouth grin) (smile <u>sad</u> face cheerful)

6 (repeat argue shout frighten) (dissolve dispute agree again) 6 ☐

7 (endeavour fail trust believe) (state try succeed attempt) 7 ☐

8 (allow avow attempt alloy) (permit forbid please create) 8 ☐

9 (tide seaside beach ebb) (splash drench paddle flow) 9 ☐

10 (light dawn morning evening) (awake dusk arise sleepy) 10 ☐

Q. 11–15
word codes

Work out these codes. The code used in each question is different. Use the alphabet to help you.

A B C D E F G H I J K L M N O P Q R S T U V W X Y Z

Example If DWU is the code for BUS, what does EQCEJ mean? __COACH__

11 If AYR is the code for CAT, what does BME mean?

_____ 11 ☐

12 If EHRG is the code for FISH, what does BQZA mean?

_____ 12 ☐

13 If PNWZA is the code for TRADE, what does YDKEN mean?

_____ 13 ☐

14 If QRWJC is the code for STYLE, what does NPMSB mean?

_____ 14 ☐

15 If ZXV is the code for ACE, what does EVG mean?

_____ 15 ☐

MARK ☐

Q. 16–20 time problems

Here is part of a train timetable for trains running between Skipton and Leeds.

SX means the train does not stop there on a Saturday.
FO means the train only stops at that station on a Friday.

Work out the answers.

	Train A	Train B	Train C	Train D	Train E
Skipton depart	07:05	07:32	07:50	08:05	08:18
Cononley	07:10	07:37 FO	07:55	08:10	08:23 FO
Steeton	07:15	07:42	08:03	08:20	08:28
Keighley	07:20	07:49	08:10	08:28	08:33
Crossflatts	07:26 SX	07:57 FO	08:18 SX		
Bingley	07:33	08:05	08:25	08:48	08:50
Saltaire	07:40	08:15 FO	08:35	08:55	
Shipley	07:47	08:24	08:45 SX	09:02	09:05
Leeds arrive	07:58	08:35	08:56	09:13	09:17

FO – Fridays only
SX – Saturdays excepted

16 Which train completes the journey from Skipton to Leeds in the shortest time?

Train _____ | 16 |

17 If you were travelling from Skipton to Saltaire on Tuesday, which two trains would you avoid?

Trains _____ and _____ | 17 |

18 If you were travelling from Steeton to Shipley on a Saturday, which train would you avoid?

Train _____ | 18 |

19 If school in Shipley starts at 09:00 and you live in Keighley, which is the latest train you can catch to get to school in time?

Train _____ | 19 |

20 Which train would not get you to Keighley by half past eight in the morning?

Train _____ | 20 |

MARK _____

MARK
✓ OR ✗

Q. 21–25

sorting
information

Read the information below carefully. Then answer the questions.

Alice, Bobby, Chris, Dylan and Emma are five friends. Alice, Bobby and Emma like football. Alice, Bobby and Dylan like running. Dylan and Bobby like tennis. Chris likes none of these. Chris and Emma both like cricket.

21 Who likes just tennis and running? _____ | 21 ☐

22 Which football players don't play cricket?

_____ and _____ | 22 ☐

23 Who likes most sports?

_____ | 23 ☐

24 Which two people share a liking for running and tennis?

_____ and _____ | 24 ☐

25 Who has only one sporting interest?

_____ | 25 ☐

Q. 26–30

spot the
word

A four-letter word is hidden in each of these sentences. You will find the hidden word at the end of one word and the beginning of the next. Underline the hidden word and then write it on the line.

Example Daniel <u>ende</u>d his speech with a joke.   <u>lend</u>

26 We all drew the scenic landscape in the sketchbooks. _____ | 26 ☐

27 You should help one another whenever you can. _____ | 27 ☐

28 They had hidden their treasure near to a great oak. _____ | 28 ☐

29 Every May our parents take us to Chester Zoo. _____ | 29 ☐

30 Dad explained that omelettes are made from eggs. _____ | 30 ☐

MARK ☐

MARK
✓ OR ✗

Q. 31–35

complete the sentence

Underline **one** word in **each** set of brackets to make the sentence sensible.

Example The (plumber <u>electrician</u> baker) repaired the (<u>light</u> loaf sink) so that we could (lamp hear <u>see</u>) again.

31 The (builder soldier wizard) said the (spatula spell spelling) would not work without the magic (soup water potion).

31 ☐

32 A (medal ribbon stamp) is (sold lent awarded) for (valour promising running) in battle.

32 ☐

33 The (intend internet inside) is very (social brief useful) for finding (facts keys outside).

33 ☐

34 The kind (sheriff emperor employer) ruled over his (empire umpire perspire) with (ferocity fairness cruelty) and justice.

34 ☐

35 In (summer hot winter) the (temperature thermometer sunlight) is too (hot cold heat) for sledging.

35 ☐

Q. 36–40

symbol codes

The word **STUPOR** is written as $\frac{3}{4}$ $\frac{1}{2}$ $\frac{7}{8}$ $\frac{1}{4}$ $\frac{5}{8}$ $\frac{3}{8}$ in code. Use the same code to work out the hidden words.

36 $\frac{1}{4}$ $\frac{5}{8}$ $\frac{3}{4}$ $\frac{1}{2}$ _____

36 ☐

37 $\frac{3}{4}$ $\frac{1}{2}$ $\frac{5}{8}$ $\frac{1}{4}$ _____

37 ☐

38 $\frac{1}{2}$ $\frac{5}{8}$ $\frac{1}{4}$ $\frac{3}{4}$ _____

38 ☐

39 $\frac{3}{4}$ $\frac{1}{4}$ $\frac{5}{8}$ $\frac{1}{2}$ _____

39 ☐

40 $\frac{1}{4}$ $\frac{5}{8}$ $\frac{1}{2}$ $\frac{3}{4}$ _____

40 ☐

Q. 41–45

odd ones out

Two words in each question do **not** belong with the rest. Underline these **two** words.

Example horrid nasty <u>kind</u> mean unfriendly <u>helpful</u>

41 devour	nibble	fast	vomit	consume	41 ☐
42 precious	treasured	rubbish	cherished	debris	42 ☐
43 disgust	gladden	loathe	delight	thrill	43 ☐
44 luxury	poverty	opulence	destitution	affluence	44 ☐
45 noun	sentence	verb	adjective	paragraph	45 ☐

MARK ☐

MARK
✓ OR ✗

Q. 46–50 always has	Look at the word in **bold**. Underline **one** option in the brackets. It must describe what the word in bold **always has**. **Example** A **lake** always has (boats <u>water</u> ducks swimmers fish).

46 A **biped** always has (four feet a bicycle shoes two feet a tail). 46 ☐

47 A **police officer** always has (handcuffs a uniform a car a job a helmet). 47 ☐

48 A **timetable** always has (tables trains times buses words). 48 ☐

49 A **melody** always has (a tune a singer an instrument sheet music). 49 ☐

50 **Money** in a purse always has (notes value coins 50p £1). 50 ☐

Q. 51–55
word grids

Fit each set of words into the grid. The words should read across and down.

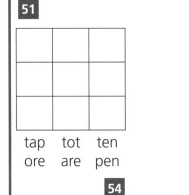

51

tap   tot   ten
ore   are   pen

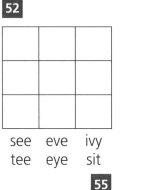

52

see   eve   ivy
tee   eye   sit

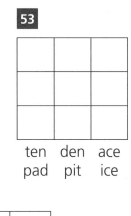

53

ten   den   ace
pad   pit   ice

54

aha   hew   apt
peg   two   ago

55

yet   eye   dew
wet   dry   rye

51 ☐
52 ☐
53 ☐
54 ☐
55 ☐

Q. 56–60
analogies

Underline **one** word in **each** set of brackets to complete these analogies.

Example Arrive is to (<u>depart</u> plane speed) as come is to (run hurry <u>go</u>).

56 We is to (our their your) as he is to (his her theirs). 56 ☐

57 Foot is to (toe ankle leg) as hand is to (wrist thumb shoulder). 57 ☐

58 Coal is to (gravel mine electricity) as stone is to (forest builder quarry). 58 ☐

59 Fruit is to (pare pair pear) as precipitation is to (rain reign rein). 59 ☐

60 Fish are to (pond scales shoal) as deer are to (convent herd convey). 60 ☐

MARK ☐

MARK
✓ OR ✗

Q. 61–65
word meanings

Each of these words can have **two** meanings. Write the numbers of the two meanings in the table below.

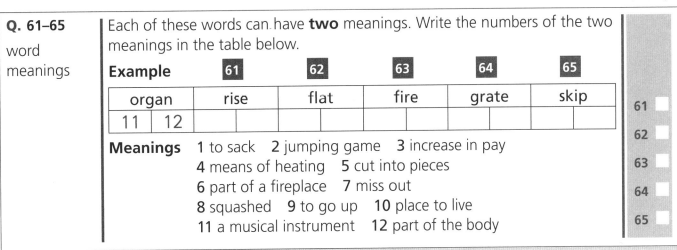

Example	61	62	63	64	65
organ	rise	flat	fire	grate	skip
11	12										

Meanings 1 to sack   2 jumping game   3 increase in pay
4 means of heating   5 cut into pieces
6 part of a fireplace   7 miss out
8 squashed   9 to go up   10 place to live
11 a musical instrument   12 part of the body

61
62
63
64
65

Q. 66–70
word categories

Underline the **general** word in each row, which is the word that includes all the others.

Example banana   apple   <u>fruit</u>   raspberry   pear   kiwi

66   cruiser   tanker   ship   battleship   tug   ferry

67   science   chemistry   physics   biology   botany   geology

68   bus   taxi   ferry   lorry   ambulance   vehicle

69   teaching   dentistry   profession   law   accountancy   medicine

70   great   minuscule   hungry   empty   green   adjective

66
67
68
69
70

Q. 71–75
which word

Two words **cannot** be made from the word in CAPITALS. Underline these words. You may only use each letter once.

Example AIRPORT   rip   <u>park</u>   trio   pair   <u>portal</u>   roar

71   CONTAINMENT   meant   comment   mention   count   attic   manic

72   SENTINEL   tense   lint   tinsel   lens   steal   steel   least   nest

73   ORCHESTRA   choir   stretch   carts   arches   score   starch

74   REASONING   soaring   grinning   string   grain   sinner   singer

75   PERIMETER   metric   remit   prime   primer   retire   emperor

71
72
73
74
75

MARK

MARK
✓ OR ✗

Q. 76–80

interpreting graphs

This bar chart shows the number of children in each year group at Wood Grove Primary School. Study the chart. Then answer the questions.

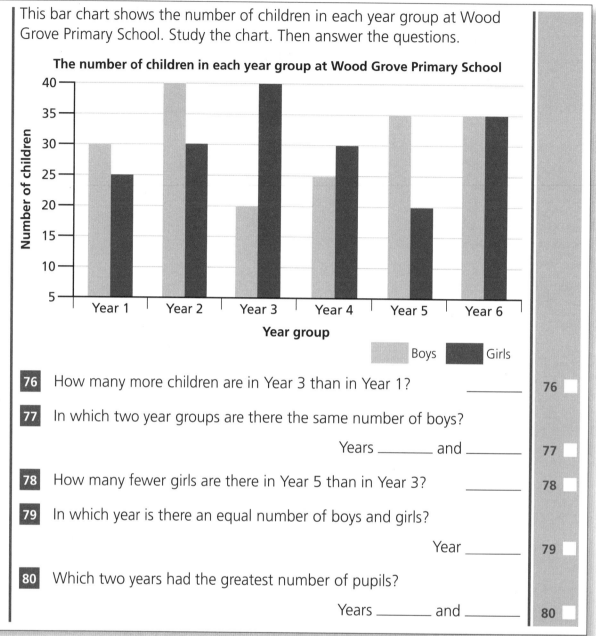

The number of children in each year group at Wood Grove Primary School

Boys Girls

76 | How many more children are in Year 3 than in Year 1? | _____ | 76 ☐

77 | In which two year groups are there the same number of boys? |
Years _____ and _____ | 77 ☐

78 | How many fewer girls are there in Year 5 than in Year 3? | _____ | 78 ☐

79 | In which year is there an equal number of boys and girls? |
Year _____ | 79 ☐

80 | Which two years had the greatest number of pupils? |
Years _____ and _____ | 80 ☐

Q. 81–85

word connections

Underline the **one** word from the brackets that fits best with the three words at the start.

Example feed eat scoff (hate mock laugh false <u>devour</u>)

81 | kindness benevolence goodwill (spite charity hatred silliness worth) | 81 ☐

82 | ruler chief head (foot protractor commander soldier hat) | 82 ☐

83 | flag pennant ensign (normal picture queen salute standard) | 83 ☐

84 | rubbish litter junk (debris nonsense boat dustbin reject) | 84 ☐

85 | run walk sprint (cycle drive jog roller-skate fly) | 85 ☐

MARK ☐

MARK
✓ OR ✗

Q. 86–90

sorting information

Read the information below carefully. Tick (✓) true, false or unknown for each statement. Tick one only.

There are five children. Their names are Amina, Billy, Corey, Daisy and Ella. Their teacher measures their heights and these are the results. Amina is shorter than Billy but taller than Ella. Corey is taller than Amina but not as tall as Billy. Daisy is taller than Ella but shorter than Amina.

		true	false	unknown	
86	Daisy is the second tallest.	☐	☐	☐	86 ☐
87	Amina is in the middle.	☐	☐	☐	87 ☐
88	Ella is taller than her mother.	☐	☐	☐	88 ☐
89	Billy is the tallest in the group.	☐	☐	☐	89 ☐
90	Except for Ella, Corey is the shortest.	☐	☐	☐	90 ☐

Q. 91–95

missing three-letter words

In each of these sentences, the word in CAPITALS has three letters missing. These three letters make a real three-letter word. Write the three-letter word on the line.

Example My father SED me a photo of my mother.   _HOW_

91	Mum has an inhaler to help with her BRHING.	_____	91 ☐
92	Gemma's hair looked lovely with a side PING.	_____	92 ☐
93	A fierce gale was BING and lifted the man's hat off.	_____	93 ☐
94	The SIER saluted smartly as the general approached.	_____	94 ☐
95	The lonesome cat was SED by the barking dogs.	_____	95 ☐

Q. 96–100

mixed-up sentences

Two words must swap places for each sentence to make sense. Underline these **two** words in each sentence.

Example The <u>bone</u> growled softly as he approached the <u>dog</u>.

96	The clock chimed as the bell struck one.	96 ☐
97	The horse led the jockey by the reins around the field.	97 ☐
98	We are getting time by saving the work done now.	98 ☐
99	Is that your gate leaning against the big bicycle?	99 ☐
100	The question to your answer is that I really don't know.	100 ☐

MARK ☐

PROGRESS PAPER 9 TOTAL ☐

END OF TEST

START HERE

MARK
✓ OR ✗

Q. 1–5

alphabetical order

Number the words in each line in alphabetical order if the **words** were written **backwards**. Use the alphabet to help you.

Example ZINC CANE CAB WET FLEA APE
3 4 2 6 1 5

A B C D E F G H I J K L M N O P Q R S T U V W X Y Z

1 BABY GROUP MILE FALL FAINT BRAG
☐ ☐ ☐ ☐ ☐ ☐

2 TALCUM NAPKIN BOTTLE TODDLER MILK BURP
☐ ☐ ☐ ☐ ☐ ☐

3 SOLDIER PLACE DOWN TERRIFY GHOST REAL
☐ ☐ ☐ ☐ ☐ ☐

4 LAMP TORCH CANDLE LIGHT BEAM BULB
☐ ☐ ☐ ☐ ☐ ☐

5 BLOOM HARM POEM DIM CHASM HUM
☐ ☐ ☐ ☐ ☐ ☐

1 ☐
2 ☐
3 ☐
4 ☐
5 ☐

Q. 6–10

sorting information

Read the information below carefully. Tick (✓) true, false or unknown for each statement. Tick one only.

Sam, Lauren and Henryk love football. They go to their football club at 5 p.m. Sam is never late for football club. On Monday Henryk was late. Lauren was late on Tuesday.

		true	false	unknown
6	Sam is sometimes late for football club.	☐	☐	☐
7	Henryk sometimes arrives after Lauren.	☐	☐	☐
8	Lauren is never late for football club.	☐	☐	☐
9	Henryk always arrives after Lauren.	☐	☐	☐
10	Sam arrived before Henryk on Monday.	☐	☐	☐

6 ☐
7 ☐
8 ☐
9 ☐
10 ☐

MARK ☐

Progress Papers
Answers

Verbal Reasoning 2

Schofield&Sims

Progress Papers in Verbal Reasoning 2

Notes for parents, tutors, teachers and other helpers

This pull-out book contains correct answers to all the questions in **Progress Papers in Verbal Reasoning 2**, and is designed to assist you, the adult helper, as you mark the child's work. Once the child has become accustomed to the method of working, you may wish to give him or her direct access to this pull-out section.

When marking, put a tick or a cross in the tinted column on the far right of the question page. **Only one mark is available for each question**. Sub-total boxes at the foot of each page will help you to add marks quickly. You can then fill in the total marks at the end of the paper. The total score is out of 100 and can easily be turned into a percentage. The child's progress can be recorded using the **Progress chart** on page 52.

The child should aim to spend between 40 and 75 minutes on each paper, but may need more time, or more than one session, to complete the paper. The child should try to work on each paper when feeling fresh and free from distraction.

How to use the pull-out answers

This booklet contains answers to all the questions in the book, as well as footnotes to help with marking. Where the child has answered a question incorrectly, take time to look at the question and answer together and work out how the correct answer was achieved.

By working through the tests and corresponding answers, the child will start to recognise the clues that he or she should look for next time. These skills can then be put into practice by moving on to the next paper, as the difficulty increases incrementally throughout the series.

When a paper has been marked, notice if there are any topics that are proving particularly tricky. You may wish to complete some targeted practice in those areas, by focusing on that particular topic as it appears in each paper. For example, if a child has struggled with word meanings, but answered all other questions accurately, you may wish to target only word meanings questions in your next practice session. The **Topics chart** at the back of the book makes it easy to tailor practice to the child's individual needs.

This book of answers is a pull-out section from
Progress Papers in Verbal Reasoning 2

Published by **Schofield & Sims Ltd**, Dogley Mill, Fenay Bridge, Huddersfield HD8 0NQ, UK

Telephone 01484 607080

www.schofieldandsims.co.uk

First published in 2016

Copyright © Schofield & Sims Ltd 2016

Author: **Patrick Berry**

Patrick Berry has asserted his moral right under the Copyright, Designs and Patents Act, 1988, to be identified as the author of this work.

Design by **Oxford Designers and Illustrators**

ISBN 978 07217 1280 2

Printed in the UK by **Wyndeham Grange Ltd**, Southwick, West Sussex

British Library Catalogue in Publication Data:
A catalogue record for this book is available from the British Library.

Progress Paper 7

1	task	
2	reef	
3	here	
4	neat	
5	ache	
6	L	N
7	P	N
8	T	V
9	VW	ZA
10	ED	BA
11	potatoes	gardener
12	she	I
13	shopping	mobile
14	asleep	angry
15	had	were
16	chuck	
17	rain	
18	plan	
19	handsome	
20	precise	
21	31	37
22	25	30
23	16	11
24	$5\frac{3}{4}$	$6\frac{1}{2}$
25	30	36
26	January	
27	tricycle	
28	canal	
29	baby	
30	teacher	
31	cent	euro
32	terrapin	platypus
33	ash	birch
34	spaghetti	cereal
35	lemonade	water
36	T	
37	D	
38	D	
39	E	
40	R	

Paper 7 – continued

41	gigantic	vast
42	wise	sensible
43	angry	enraged
44	fearless	brave
45	identical	same
46	STALE	
47	TEALS	
48	SLATE	
49	LEAST	
50	TALES	
51	tries	
52	star	
53	retired	
54	seam	
55	plug	
56	SLAY	SLAP
57	TRAY	PRAY
	or PRAM	PRAY
58	TYRE	TORE
59	DALE	DAME
	or MOLE	DOLE
60	TALL	TALE
	or TALL	MALL

Accept any accurate response to word chain questions.

61	gills
62	a frame
63	feet
64	wet
65	walls
66	EAR
67	EAT
68	WAR
69	DEN
70	TIN
71	C
72	D
73	D
74	D
75	E

Paper 7 – continued

76	disease
77	spotless
78	answer
79	dally
80	broccoli
81	BLEAT*
82	STABLE*
83	BEETLES*
84	HIPPO*
85	GALLERY*
86	spares
87	eager
88	mentor
89	leapt
90	intent

91	(across) boa	ear	eke	
	(down) bee	oak	are	
92	(across) err	bay	bye	
	(down) ebb	ray	rye	
93	(across) act	nor	toy	
	(down) ant	coo	try	
94	(across) ego	nod	doe	
	(down) end	goo	ode	
95	(across) art	due	den	
	(down) add	rue	ten	

96	news
97	post
98	some
99	hand
100	bar

*spellings must be correct

Progress Paper 8

#		
1	2011	2013
2	2010	
3	2009	2010
4	2013	
5	girls	

#						
6	5	3	1	6	4	2
7	6	5	4	1	3	2
8	5	3	2	1	6	4
9	4	6	2	5	3	1
10	4	2	5	3	1	6

#	
11	sun
12	tea
13	work
14	car
15	wind

#		
16	nine	house
17	allotment	cruiser
18	hexagon	run
19	gram	centimetre
20	meal	cat

#	
21	germ
22	ouch
23	them
24	slap
25	test

#	
26	CREAM
27	HIDE
28	BREAD
29	BEARD
30	BOWEL

#	
31	TRIM
32	RITE
33	PIER
34	MINT
35	TEMPER

#			
36	mango	apple	plum
37	cobbler	carpenter	tiler
38	swede	sprout	cabbage
39	scarlet	cerise	purple
40	eraser	ruler	staple

Paper 8 – continued

#	
41	log
42	vessel
43	clutch
44	post
45	cloak

#	
46	Daniel
47	Carrie
48	Elle
49	Ben
50	Arfan

#		
51	prone	carpet
52	traitor	parent
53	field	dirtied
54	defence	centre
55	depend	denoted

#		
56	prey	mouse
57	author	poet
58	tadpole	caterpillar
59	bullet	arrow
60	easy	anxious

#		
61	BUSH	LARD
62	BOND	BUOY
63	BARD	HELLO
64	POND	COULD
65	BAY	PLUMB

#		
66	XT	YW
67	HI	SR
68	WZ	AD
69	JF	LI
70	AWV	VYX

#	
71	AND
72	OUR
73	TAR
74	MEN
75	ERA

#		
76	sweet	sugary
77	beautiful	pretty
78	imprison	incarcerate
79	wise	sensible
80	trivial	paltry

Paper 8 – continued

#			
81	Don't	litter	street
82	pupils	books	library
83	feet	corns	I
84	cat	purred	lapped
85	barber	hair	smart

#	
86	120p
87	140p
88	180p
89	225p
90	90p

#		
91	meadow	field
92	filthy	dirty
93	guard	warder
94	firm	business
95	disguise	mask

#		
96	MINUTES	HOUR*
97	FOOTBALL	TENNIS*
98	COMPUTER	REPAIRED*
99	HOLIDAY	SPAIN*
100	DETECTIVE	MYSTERY*

*spellings must be correct

Progress Paper 9

1 LAIR*
2 SETTEE*
3 TRIANGLE*
4 WARDROBE*
5 BREAKFAST^

6 argue — agree
7 fail — succeed
8 allow — forbid
9 ebb — flow
10 dawn — dusk

11 DOG
12 CRAB
13 CHOIR
14 PROUD
15 VET

16 Train A
17 Trains B and E
18 Train C
19 Train C
20 Train E

21 Dylan
22 Alice and Bobby
23 Bobby
24 Bobby and Dylan
25 Chris

26 clan
27 very
28 dent
29 your
30 atom

31 wizard spell potion
32 medal awarded valour
33 internet useful facts
34 emperor empire fairness
35 summer temperature hot

36 POST
37 STOP
38 TOPS
39 SPOT
40 POTS

Paper 9 – continued

41 fast — vomit
42 rubbish — debris
43 disgust — loathe
44 poverty — destitution
45 sentence — paragraph

46 two feet
47 a job
48 times
49 a tune
50 value

51 (across) tap ore ten / (down) tot are pen†
52 (across) sit eve eye / (down) see ivy tee†
53 (across) pit ace den / (down) pad ice ten†
54 (across) aha peg two / (down) apt hew ago†
55 (across) dew rye yet / (down) dry eye wet†

56 our — his
57 ankle — wrist
58 mine — quarry
59 pear — rain
60 shoal — herd

61 3 9
62 8 10
63 1 4
64 5 6
65 2 7

66 ship
67 science
68 vehicle
69 profession
70 adjective

71 comment — count
72 steal — least
73 choir — stretch
74 grinning — string
75 metric — emperor

Paper 9 – continued

76 5
77 Years 5 and 6
78 20
79 Year 6
80 Years 2 and 6

81 charity
82 commander
83 standard
84 debris
85 jog

86 false
87 true
88 unknown
89 true
90 false

91 EAT
92 ART
93 LOW
94 OLD
95 CAR

96 clock — bell
97 horse — jockey
98 getting — saving
99 gate — bicycle
100 question — answer

*spellings must be correct

†across and down words can also be the other way round

Progress Paper 10

1. 6 4 1 3 5 2
2. 3 4 1 6 2 5
3. 4 1 3 6 5 2
4. 5 3 2 6 4 1
5. 3 4 1 2 5 6
6. false
7. unknown
8. false
9. unknown
10. true
11. ART
12. END
13. END
14. PUT
15. AGE
16. CHIN   CHIP
17. MALE   MILE
18. BOTH   BATH
19. BLOT   BLOW
20. HONE   HOLE

Accept any accurate response to word chain questions.

21. LIVE
22. BELL
23. FUEL
24. KALE
25. BULK
26. person   fable
27. obese   plump
28. mystery   agreement
29. keep   retain
30. delighted   happy
31. easy   difficult
32. few   many
33. juvenile   adult
34. ancestor   descendant
35. sold   bought
36. 6   8
37. 3   5
38. 1   4
39. 7   9
40. 2   10

Paper 10 – continued

41. G
42. P
43. W
44. H
45. T
46. pale*
47. hurt*
48. cough*
49. slot*
50. toad*
51. rain
52. roller
53. heater
54. loots
55. tatty
56. PEASANT
57. PANTING
58. FIEND
59. DIED
60. SHAM
61. DOCTOR   SEVERAL*
62. USING   PERMISSION*
63. UPSET   EXAMINATION*
64. DIESEL   CARRIAGES*
65. YACHT   GLOBE*
66. 10:00   11:20
67. 11:40   13:30
68. 13:15   13:55
69. 11:00   12:20
70. 12:57   14:07
71. mangetout
72. drive
73. hearing
74. education
75. tame
76. speak   sentence
77. street   month
78. magazine   pigeon
79. ditch   rifle
80. mansion   angry

Paper 10 – continued

81. globe
82. grave
83. jam
84. plain
85. rest
86. head   ache
87. par   snip
88. in   tend
89. foot   ball
90. war   ring
91. 4   10
92. $1\frac{1}{4}$ $\frac{5}{8}$
93. 49   64
94. 240   0
95. 360   2160
96. food
97. musician
98. rodents
99. spice
100. plant

*spellings must be correct

Progress Paper 11

1	vest
2	wash
3	here
4	leap
5	mask

6	STAGE
7	FRIGHT
8	FLOUR
9	PROUD
10	DESIGN

11	slavery	freedom
12	healthy	ill
13	release	arrest
14	descend	ascend
15	fragile	robust

16	Phoebe
17	English
18	Evie
19	Mia
20	French

21	WEEKS	YEAR*
22	QUEEN	PALACE*
23	INJURIES	HOSPITAL*
24	SURGEON	ANKLE*
25	LONDON	ENGLAND*

26	land
27	present
28	ace
29	bound
30	tap

31	LK	HM
32	SI	VF
33	LF	HK
34	PK	NM
35	ZZ	BC

36	SEA	PLACE
37	SIZE	SNIPE
38	RUN	BAIT
39	WATER	MOIST
40	DIED	STROVE

Paper 11 – *continued*

41	solution	answer
42	query	question
43	supple	elastic
44	sentence	paragraph
45	sea	ocean

46	flower	tree
47	pilot	captain
48	orchestra	choir
49	deciduous	coniferous
50	countryside	urban

51	7
52	60
53	$4\frac{1}{2}$
54	126
55	60

56	*(across)* cable crash enter *(down)* cycle blast ether
57	*(across)* pence rhino sieve *(down)* parts noise evoke
58	*(across)* holly spook easel *(down)* haste looks yokel[†]
59	*(across)* local being lapel *(down)* libel crisp legal[†]
60	*(across)* river total radar *(down)* rotor voted ruler[†]

61	D
62	C
63	C
64	C
65	D

66	106 minutes
67	12:58
68	15:03
69	137 minutes
70	22:57

71	cascade	cataract
72	flock	staff
73	plate	tureen
74	spoon	knife
75	bureau	wardrobe

Paper 11 – *continued*

76	cricket umpire out
77	hot swimming cool
78	books library dusted
79	athletes medals games
80	shoes cobbler repaired

81	pass	word
82	side	ways
83	out	ward
84	in	side
85	way	side

86	VKIGT
87	GRQNHB
88	IPITLERX
89	YXYLLK
90	IZFTZQ

91	SHOT	SLOT
	or SLOW	BLOW
	or SLOW	SLOT
92	MELT	BELT
	or BEAT	BELT
	or MOAT	BOAT
93	GIVE	GAVE
94	BALL	BAIL
95	DAME	TAME
	or DAME	DIME

Accept any accurate response to word chain questions.

96	30
97	yellow and orange
98	red and green
99	blue
100	orange, blue, red, yellow, green

*spellings must be correct

[†]*across* and *down* words can also be the other way round

Progress Paper 12

1	mystery	puzzle
2	similarity	synonym
3	footwear	gloves
4	circle	cone
5	rainbow	scarlet
6	hum	bug
7	reason	able
8	car	go
9	ear	wig
10	eye	lid
11	SOLID	BRAIN
12	DRIED	FRIGHT
13	COAST	STRAPS
	or COATS	STRAPS
14	TRIBES	TABLE
15	CHAIR	PRICES
16	D	
17	D	
18	Y	
19	M	
20	H	
21	CH	
22	IN	
23	TY	
24	ER	
25	LE	
26	(caramels) camels*	
27	(suite) suit*	
28	(window) widow*	
29	(hunted) haunted*	
30	(collage) college*	
31	15	
32	13	
33	10	
34	135	
35	5	
36	15827463	
37	15278463	
38	72518463	
39	87416352	
40	46823715	

Paper 12 – continued

41	4	9
42	1	7
43	2	5
44	3	6
45	8	10
46	U	
47	ST	
48	DY	
49	TQ	
50	ON	
51	sergeant	weekly
52	bus	wind
53	mug	wall
54	tenth	group
55	lorry	decade
56	sand	
57	thin	
58	rein	
59	lamb	
60	epic	
61	interior	exterior
62	majority	minority
63	miser	spendthrift
64	imaginary	real
65	height	depth
66	shout	
67	straw	
68	soles	
69	otter	
70	throw	
71	tricycle tandem tractor	
72	kayak junk barge	
73	diving javelin volleyball	
74	whisk spatula microwave	
75	cello trombone oboe	
76	traps	
77	plentiful	
78	breather	
79	trite	
80	leash	

Paper 12 – continued

81	kind
82	look
83	rock
84	ring
85	sense
86	C
87	D
88	C
89	A
90	D
91	TWICE*
92	ELEPHANT*
93	LUNCH*
94	DANGER*
95	UNDERSTAND*
96	TIE
97	THE
98	OUT
99	ROT
100	ART or TAR

*spellings must be correct

MARK
✓ OR ✗

Q. 11–15

missing three-letter words

In each of these sentences, the word in CAPITALS has three letters missing. These three letters make a real three-letter word. Write the three-letter word on the line.

Example My father SLD me a photo of my mother. ___HOW___

11 Lily bought a lovely APMENT in the centre of town. _____   11 ☐

12 She consulted her CALAR to see which dates were free.

_____   12 ☐

13 My best FRIS are both in my class at school. _____   13 ☐

14 I spend many hours working at my COMER. _____   14 ☐

15 A MENRIE is a place like a zoo where animals are kept.

_____   15 ☐

Q. 16–20

word chains

Turn the word on the left into the word on the right. You can only change one letter at a time. Each change must result in a real word.

Example TALE ___TAKE___ ___LAKE___ LIKE

16 T H I N _____ _____ C H O P   16 ☐

17 D A L E _____ _____ M I L D   17 ☐

18 M O T H _____ _____ B A T S   18 ☐

19 P L O T _____ _____ B R O W   19 ☐

20 T O N E _____ _____ H O L Y   20 ☐

Q. 21–25

match the codes

The words below have been written in code. Which code belongs to which word? Write the answers on the lines.

BULK   FUEL   LIVE   KALE   BELL

7 3 1 4   8 4 7 7   2 5 7 4   8 6 7 2   9 6 4 7

21 7 3 1 4   is the code for _____.   21 ☐

22 8 4 7 7   is the code for _____.   22 ☐

23 9 6 4 7   is the code for _____.   23 ☐

24 2 5 7 4   is the code for _____.   24 ☐

25 8 6 7 2   is the code for _____.   25 ☐

MARK ☐

MARK
✓ OR ✗

Q. 26–30 odd ones out	Two words in each question do **not** belong with the rest. Underline these **two** words.	
	Example horrid nasty <u>kind</u> mean unfriendly <u>helpful</u>	
	26 phantom person spectre ghost fable spook wraith	26
	27 obese gaunt lean cadaverous plump haggard	27
	28 rebellion mystery mutiny revolt agreement uprising	28
	29 keep forsake retain desert abandon disown	29
	30 melancholy delighted gloomy depressed despondent happy	30

Q. 31–35 antonyms	Underline two words, **one** from **each** set of brackets, that have the **opposite** meaning.	
	Example (<u>happy</u> kind mouth grin) (smile <u>sad</u> face cheerful)	
	31 (necessary easy increase compulsory) (simple improve difficult less)	31
	32 (plural singular few several) (single married many empty)	32
	33 (tiny elderly simple juvenile) (adult minor normal clever)	33
	34 (ancestor aged prehistoric grandpa) (aunt descendant son youth)	34
	35 (pay receipt purchase sold) (buy bought shop ticket)	35

Q. 36–40 word meanings	Each of these words can have **two** meanings. Write the numbers of the two meanings in the table below.

Example

	36		37		38		39		40	
organ		iron		knot		play		tear		pine
11	12									

36

37

Meanings   1 seen in a theatre   2 to long for   3 made with string
4 the opposite of work   5 found in wood
6 used in a laundry   7 to rip   8 its ore is dug from the ground
9 liquid from the eye   10 a tree   11 a musical instrument
12 part of the body

38

39

40

MARK

MARK
✓ OR ✗

Q. 41–45

missing letters

The same letter will end the first word and begin the next word. Write the letter.

Example PAN (_T_) URN

41	KIN (__) AP	SON (__) APE	41 ☐
42	LEA (__) EAR	SEE (__) LEASE	42 ☐
43	DRA (__) ASP	SE (__) EAR	43 ☐
44	PINC (__) ARROW	ARC (__) ERE	44 ☐
45	SOR (__) AWNY	PAIN (__) OMB	45 ☐

Q. 46–50

rhyming words

Add **one** word to complete each sentence. The word you add must rhyme with the word in CAPITALS.

Example TOAD   The lorry was carrying a heavy _load_ .

46	HAIL	The sick man's face looked drawn and _____ .	46 ☐
47	SHIRT	He couldn't run because he had _____ his leg.	47 ☐
48	OFF	Filip couldn't go to school because of his bad _____ .	48 ☐
49	YACHT	Leah put some coins in the _____ to pay for her ticket.	49 ☐
50	CODE	A big fat _____ sat on the log.	50 ☐

Q. 51–55

make a word

Look at how the second word is made from the first word in each pair. Complete the third pair in the same way. Write the answers on the lines.

Example (fright rights) (flight lights) (height _eights_)

51	(cleaver leave)	(grate rat)	(trains _____)	51 ☐
52	(halt hall)	(stake slake)	(rotter _____)	52 ☐
53	(singles singer)	(helpful helper)	(heating _____)	53 ☐
54	(garb brag)	(time emit)	(stool _____)	54 ☐
55	(dodder totter)	(dread treat)	(daddy _____)	55 ☐

MARK ☐

MARK
✓ OR ✗

Q. 56–60 take a letter	Read the clue in brackets. Remove **one** letter from the word in CAPITALS to make a new word that matches the clue. Write the new word on the line. **Example** BRIGHT (correct) <u>RIGHT</u>

56 PLEASANT (a person who worked on the land) _____ 56 ☐

57 PAINTING (short of breath) _____ 57 ☐

58 FRIEND (an evil person) _____ 58 ☐

59 DRIED (stopped living) _____ 59 ☐

60 SHAME (false) _____ 60 ☐

Q. 61–65 jumbled words in sentences	The letters of the words in CAPITALS have been mixed up. Write the **two** correct words on the lines. **Example** The TERWA was too cold to WSIM in. <u>WATER</u> and <u>SWIM</u>

61 When I was ill, the TRODOC came to see me LEAVERS times.

_____ and _____ 61 ☐

62 You've been SUING my computer again without my MISSPERONI.

_____ and _____ 62 ☐

63 He was sad and SETUP when he heard that he had failed in the AMEXITONIAN.

_____ and _____ 63 ☐

64 The big SEELID engine pulled the railway GREASICAR easily.

_____ and _____ 64 ☐

65 The CHATY sailed right round the BOLGE.

_____ and _____ 65 ☐

MARK ☐

MARK
✓ OR ✗

Q. 66–70

time problems

Here is part of a train timetable showing arrivals at certain stations. The journey times between stations are the same for each train.

Some arrival times are missing. Fill in the missing times. Use the 24-hour clock.

		Train A	Train B	Train C	Train D
66	Amberley			12:30	13:10
67	Baddesley	10:20		12:50	
68	Caverley	10:45	12:05		
69	Dibbsley			13:30	14:10
70	Eggsley	11:37			14:47

66 ☐
67 ☐
68 ☐
69 ☐
70 ☐

Q. 71–75

analogies

Underline **one** word to complete these analogies.

Example Arrive is to depart as come is to (run hurry go hide).

71 Fruit is to kiwi as vegetable is to (green lemon mangetout meal healthy).

71 ☐

72 Pedestrian is to walk as motorist is to (wheel pavement road drive car).

72 ☐

73 Television is to sight as radio is to (digital hearing listen aerial music).

73 ☐

74 Solicitor is to law as teacher is to (classroom pupils school work education).

74 ☐

75 Leopard is to wild as poodle is to (biscuit bark park walk tame).

75 ☐

Q. 76–80

mixed-up groups

Two groups of three words have been mixed up in each question. Work out which would be the **middle** word in each group if they were in the correct order. Underline these **two** words.

Example city <u>adolescent</u> village <u>town</u> infant adult

76 paragraph yell speak word sentence whisper

76 ☐

77 year street path week month motorway

77 ☐

78 magazine ostrich book sparrow pigeon pamphlet

78 ☐

79 ditch gorge cannon pistol crack rifle

79 ☐

80 mansion angry irritated skyscraper bungalow furious

80 ☐

MARK ☐

MARK
✓ OR ✗

Q. 81–85

word connections

Underline the **one** word that fits with **both** pairs of words in brackets.

Example (heart club) (ruby emerald)   jewel brain <u>diamond</u> card brooch

81 (ball sphere) (world Earth) globe planet ring circle plate | 81 ☐

82 (vault crypt) (serious sombre) burial momentous cemetery grave earth | 82 ☐

83 (gridlock bottleneck) (toast marmalade) food stick jam preserve jar | 83 ☐

84 (clear obvious) (prairie grassland) tundra simple transparent plain wooded | 84 ☐

85 (stay remain) (relax sleep) snore rest leftovers calm peaceful | 85 ☐

Q. 86–90

join two words to make one

Circle **one** word from **each** group, which together will make a longer word.

Example (pond (dam) river)   (era down (age))

86 (head   body   two)   (pain   ache   face) | 86 ☐

87 (some   where   par)   (gave   snip   try) | 87 ☐

88 (in   vent   side)   (tend   call   press) | 88 ☐

89 (fan   foot   read)   (trip   side   ball) | 89 ☐

90 (pain   war   full)   (ring   pant   tile) | 90 ☐

Q. 91–95

number sequences

Write the next two numbers in each sequence.

Example 2 4 6 8 <u>10</u> <u>12</u>

91 1   4   2   6   3   8   ____ ____ | 91 ☐

92 20 10 5 $2\frac{1}{2}$ ____ ____ | 92 ☐

93 1   4   9   16   25   36   ____ ____ | 93 ☐

94 2   10   40   120   240   ____ ____ | 94 ☐

95 3   3   6   18   72   ____ ____ | 95 ☐

MARK ☐

MARK
✓ OR ✗

Q. 96–100 word categories	Underline the **general** word in each row, which is the word that includes all the others.	
	Example banana apple <u>fruit</u> raspberry pear kiwi	
	96 cornflakes bread cheese milk food potatoes apples rice	96
	97 composer singer pianist conductor timpanist musician	97
	98 rats rodents beavers mice squirrels hamsters gerbils	98
	99 spice ginger mace nutmeg vanilla cloves chilli garlic	99
	100 fern tree bush plant algae moss grass conifer	100

MARK ☐

END OF TEST

PROGRESS PAPER 10 TOTAL ☐

START HERE

Q. 1–5

spot the word

A four-letter word is hidden in each of these sentences. You will find the hidden word at the end of one word and the beginning of the next. Underline the hidden word and then write it on the line.

Example Daniel <u>end</u>ed his speech with a joke.   <u>lend</u>

1   The huge stones at Stonehenge have stood for centuries.

_____   1 ☐

2   I asked my brother if it was his football that broke the window.

_____   2 ☐

3   I think they are fed up with the repeats on television.

_____   3 ☐

4   Adam's bicycle appears to have been stolen.   _____   4 ☐

5   Mum asked me to take some clothes to the charity shop.

_____   5 ☐

Q. 6–10

add a letter

Read the clue in brackets. Add **one** letter to the word in CAPITALS to make a new word that matches the clue. Write the new word on the line.

Example CANE   (lifts heavy items)   <u>CRANE</u>

6   SAGE   (somewhere to act)   _____   6 ☐

7   FIGHT   (a scare)   _____   7 ☐

8   FOUR   (make bread with it)   _____   8 ☐

9   PROD   (pleased with oneself)   _____   9 ☐

10   DEIGN   (to draw or plan something)   _____   10 ☐

Q. 11–15

antonyms

Underline two words, **one** from **each** set of brackets, that have the **opposite** meaning.

Example (<u>happy</u> kind mouth grin)   (smile <u>sad</u> face cheerful)

11   (slavery prison jail punishment)   (outside freedom warder cell)   11 ☐

12   (good cheerful healthy clean)   (ill happy doctor immaculate)   12 ☐

13   (release stop freedom disarm)   (question merciful arrest attack)   13 ☐

14   (depart desert detain descend)   (mount ascend ascertain assert)   14 ☐

15   (fracture fail fragile break)   (accident robust reappear bandage)   15 ☐

MARK ☐

MARK
✓ OR ✗

| **Q. 16–20** | This chart shows the favourite subjects of six children. |
| interpreting tables | Answer the questions. |

	Maths	English	History	Art	Geography	French	Science
Beth	✓	✓		✓		✓	✓
Syed		✓	✓		✓	✓	
Evie		✓		✓			✓
Mia	✓	✓	✓		✓		✓
Tom	✓	✓	✓	✓			✓
Phoebe	✓	✓	✓	✓	✓		✓

16 Who likes the most subjects? _____ 16 ☐

17 Which subject is the group's favourite? _____ 17 ☐

18 Who likes the least number of subjects? _____ 18 ☐

19 Who likes maths but not art or French? _____ 19 ☐

20 Which subject is least liked? _____ 20 ☐

| **Q. 21–25** | The letters of the words in CAPITALS have been mixed up. Write the **two** correct words on the lines. |
| jumbled words in sentences | **Example** The TERWA was too cold to WSIM in. _WATER_ and _SWIM_ |

21 There are 52 SEEKW in a AREY.

_____ and _____ 21 ☐

22 The ENQUE lives in a grand LAPEAC.

_____ and _____ 22 ☐

23 He had serious JINERUSI and was taken by ambulance to TAILSHOP.

_____ and _____ 23 ☐

24 The GONURSE operated on the patient's broken KLEAN.

_____ and _____ 24 ☐

25 DOOLNN is the capital city of NDANGLE.

_____ and _____ 25 ☐

MARK ☐

MARK
✓ OR ✗

Q. 26–30

word connections

Underline the **one** word that fits with **both** pairs of words in brackets.

Example (heart club) (ruby emerald)   jewel brain <u>diamond</u> card brooch

26 (alight touchdown) (earth country)   plane plot dirt land voyage | 26 ☐

27 (now currently) (gift donation)   package present today cost immediately | 27 ☐

28 (brilliant superb) (lob volley)   remarkable ace net bright sport | 28 ☐

29 (leap vault) (tied roped)   bound somersault fettered tomb escape | 29 ☐

30 (faucet stopcock) (knock rap)   water blow beat collide tap | 30 ☐

Q. 31–35

letter sequences

Write the next two items in each sequence. Use the alphabet to help you.

Example AB   CD   EF   GH   <u>IJ</u>   <u>KL</u>

A B C D E F G H I J K L M N O P Q R S T U V W X Y Z

31 FA   BC   XE   TG   PI   _____   _____ | 31 ☐

32 DX   GU   JR   MO   PL   _____   _____ | 32 ☐

33 FG   BL   XQ   TV   PA   _____   _____ | 33 ☐

34 ZA   XC   VE   TG   RI   _____   _____ | 34 ☐

35 MN   PP   RS   UU   WX   _____   _____ | 35 ☐

Q. 36–40

move a letter

Take **one** letter from the first word and put it in the second word to make two new words. Write the two new words on the lines.

Example LIME and ZOO become <u>LIE</u> and <u>ZOOM</u>.

36 SEAL and PACE become   _____ and _____. | 36 ☐

37 SEIZE and SNIP become   _____ and _____. | 37 ☐

38 RUIN and BAT become   _____ and _____. | 38 ☐

39 WAITER and MOST become _____ and _____. | 39 ☐

40 DRIED and STOVE become _____ and _____. | 40 ☐

MARK ☐

MARK
✓ OR ✗

Q. 41–45
odd ones out

Two words in each question do **not** belong with the rest. Underline these **two** words.

Example horrid   nasty   <u>kind</u>   mean   unfriendly   <u>helpful</u>

41 issue   solution   difficulty   problem   answer   complication | 41 ☐

42 response   reply   retort   query   rejoinder   question | 42 ☐

43 stiff   unyielding   supple   elastic   firm   inflexible   rigid | 43 ☐

44 sentence   comma   colon   bracket   paragraph   hyphen | 44 ☐

45 sea   river   ocean   stream   rivulet   creek | 45 ☐

Q. 46–50
analogies

Underline **one** word in **each** set of brackets to complete these analogies.

Example Arrive is to (<u>depart</u> plane speed) as come is to (run hurry <u>go</u>).

46 Petal is to (flower bike grass) as leaf is to (page enormous tree). | 46 ☐

47 Airliner is to (steward pilot hostess) as ship is to (anchor look-out captain). | 47 ☐

48 Instrumentalists are to (herd orchestra crowd) as singers are to (group choir set). | 48 ☐

49 Oak is to (tree large deciduous) as fir is to (coniferous pointed green). | 49 ☐

50 Rural is to (countryside fields river) as (people houses urban) is to city. | 50 ☐

Q. 51–55
number
connections

Work out how the numbers are connected. Then fill in the gaps.

Example	2	6	3		5	50	10		6	48	8

51	3	7	21		5	9	45		6		42
52	20	55	75		16	32	48		30		90
53	96	48	24		35	$17\frac{1}{2}$	$8\frac{3}{4}$		9		$2\frac{1}{4}$
54	5	100	20		4	52	13		9		14
55	40	50	30		16	20	12		48		36

51 ☐
52 ☐
53 ☐
54 ☐
55 ☐

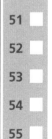

MARK ☐

MARK
✓ OR ✗

Q. 56–60

word grids

Fit each set of words into the grid. The words should read across and down.

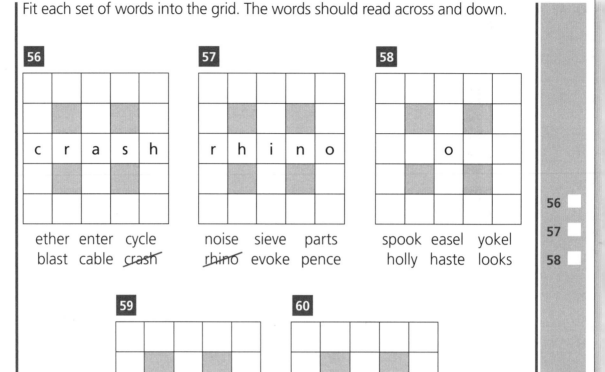

56

c	r	a	s	h

ether enter cycle
blast cable ~~crash~~

57

r	h	i	n	o

noise sieve parts
~~rhino~~ evoke pence

58

			o	

spook easel yokel
holly haste looks

59

		i		

legal local being
libel lapel crisp

60

		t		

voted river radar
rotor ruler total

56 ☐
57 ☐
58 ☐
59 ☐
60 ☐

Q. 61–65

letters for numbers

If **A** is **2**, **B** is **3**, **C** is **5**, **D** is **10** and **E** is **20**, work out these calculations. Give the answer as a letter.

Example A + B = ▪ <u> C </u>

61 4C – D = ▪   _____ 61 ☐

62 $D^2 - E - (3 \times C^2) = $ ▪   _____ 62 ☐

63 $D^2 - (C \times D) - E = C^2 + $ ▪   _____ 63 ☐

64 $3D - C^2 = $ ▪   _____ 64 ☐

65 D – C + A + B = ▪   _____ 65 ☐

MARK ☐

MARK
✓ OR ✗

Q. 66–70

time
problems

Write the missing times and journey lengths. Use the 24-hour clock.

	Train leaves at	Journey lasts	Train arrives at
66	10:47		12:33
67	11:22	96 minutes	
68		43 minutes	15:46
69	17:51		20:08
70		98 minutes	00:35

66 ☐
67 ☐
68 ☐
69 ☐
70 ☐

Q. 71–75

word
categories

Below this table are 10 words. Write each word in the correct column.

71	**72**	**73**	**74**	**75**
water	groups	crockery	cutlery	furniture

bureau   spoon   cascade   tureen   flock   staff
plate   wardrobe   knife   cataract

71 ☐
72 ☐
73 ☐
74 ☐
75 ☐

Q. 76–80

complete the
sentence

Underline **one** word in **each** set of brackets to make the sentence sensible.

Example The (plumber <u>electrician</u> baker) repaired the (<u>light</u> loaf sink) so that we could (lamp hear <u>see</u>) again.

76 During the (football snooker cricket) match the (umpire manager referee) declared the batsman to be (retired out asleep).

77 The August weather was so (hot cold awful) that we went to the local (shouting running swimming) pool to (jump smile cool) off.

78 All the (fish books cars) in the (tank library hospital) have to be taken down and (washed dusted bandaged).

79 The (athletes players soldiers) won many gold (stars medals boots) at the (show games play).

80 You take your (feet shoes car) to a (ploughman cobbler dentist) to be (repaired cleaned scraped).

76 ☐
77 ☐
78 ☐
79 ☐
80 ☐

MARK ☐

MARK
✓ OR ✗

Q. 81–85

join two words to make one

Circle **one** word from **each** group, which together will make a longer word.

Example (pond (dam) river) (era down (age))

81 (new side pass)   (out ray word)   81

82 (side board out)   (in ways up)   82

83 (good exit out)   (pass ways ward)   83

84 (in pass good)   (down side out)   84

85 (push way word)   (side ray in)   85

Q. 86–90

word codes

Work out these codes. The code used in each question is different. Use the alphabet to help you.

A B C D E F G H I J K L M N O P Q R S T U V W X Y Z

Example	bus	DWU	coach	EQCEJ

	Word	Code	Word	Code
86	monkey	OQPMGA	tiger	
87	zebra	CHEUD	donkey	
88	rhino	VLMRS	elephant	
89	giraffe	DFOXCCB	baboon	
90	tortoise	SNQSNHRD	jaguar	

86
87
88
89
90

Q. 91–95

word chains

Turn the word on the left into the word on the right. You can only change one letter at a time. Each change must result in a real word.

Example TALE _TAKE_ _LAKE_ LIKE

91 S H O W _____ _____ B L O T   91

92 M E A T _____ _____ B O L T   92

93 L I V E _____ _____ G A T E   93

94 B I L L _____ _____ S A I L   94

95 D A M P _____ _____ T I M E   95

MARK [ ]

MARK
✓ OR ✗

Q. 96–100

interpreting
graphs

The chart shows the favourite colours of a group of Year 6 pupils.
Answer the questions.

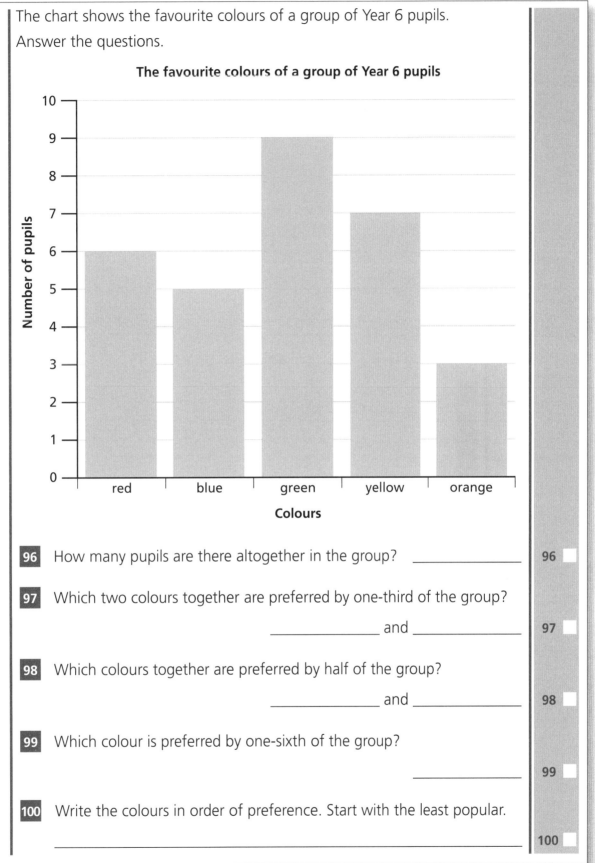

The favourite colours of a group of Year 6 pupils

41

96 How many pupils are there altogether in the group? _____   96 ☐

97 Which two colours together are preferred by one-third of the group?

_____ and _____   97 ☐

98 Which colours together are preferred by half of the group?

_____ and _____   98 ☐

99 Which colour is preferred by one-sixth of the group?

_____   99 ☐

100 Write the colours in order of preference. Start with the least popular.

_____   100 ☐

MARK ☐

END OF TEST

PROGRESS PAPER 11 TOTAL ☐

Verbal Reasoning Progress Paper 12

MARK
✓ OR ✗

Q. 1–5

odd ones out

Two words in each question do **not** belong with the rest. Underline these **two** words.

Example horrid   nasty   <u>kind</u>   mean   unfriendly   <u>helpful</u>

1 saga   mystery   story   tale   narrative   puzzle

1 ☐

2 similarity   contrary   reverse   opposite   synonym   antonym

2 ☐

3 slippers   footwear   clogs   moccasins   boots   trainers   gloves

3 ☐

4 triangle   circle   square   octagon   cone   pentagon

4 ☐

5 rainbow   red   orange   yellow   scarlet   green   indigo   blue   violet

5 ☐

Q. 6–10

join two
words to
make one

Circle **one** word from **each** group, which together will make a longer word.

Example (pond (dam) river)   (era   down   (age))

6 (tap   art   hum   mug)   (bus   top   can   bug)

6 ☐

7 (going   reason   envy   heavy)   (vied   ever   parcel   able)

7 ☐

8 (bus   van   car   train)   (went   come   go   here)

8 ☐

9 (ear   nose   eye   hand)   (weight   head   hair   wig)

9 ☐

10 (eye   nose   hand   ear)   (top   cover   lid   roof)

10 ☐

Q. 11–15

add a letter

Add the **same** letter to each pair of words in CAPITALS to make two new words. The added letter can go anywhere in the word. Write the two new words on the lines.

Example CASH and BAKE become ___CRASH___ and ___BRAKE___ .

11 SOLD and BRAN become _____ and _____ .

11 ☐

12 DIED and FIGHT become _____ and _____ .

12 ☐

13 COAT and TRAPS become _____ and _____ .

13 ☐

14 TRIES and TALE become _____ and _____ .

14 ☐

15 HAIR and PRIES become _____ and _____ .

15 ☐

MARK ☐

MARK ✓ OR ✗

Q. 16–20 letters for numbers

Work out these calculations. Give the answer as a letter.

Example If A is 4, B is 5, C is 6 and D is 9, answer this calculation.
A + B = ▢ D

16 If A is 8, B is 4, C is 12 and D is 2, answer this calculation.
(B + C) ÷ A = ▢ ______ 16 ▢

17 If A is 4, B is 6, C is 3, D is 2 and E is 9, answer this calculation.
(A × E) ÷ (C × B) = ▢ ______ 17 ▢

18 If X is 6, Y is 8, Z is 2 and P is 3, answer this calculation.
(X × Y) ÷ (P × Z) = ▢ ______ 18 ▢

19 If J is 4, K is 6, L is 2 and M is 3, answer this calculation.
(K × L) ÷ J = ▢ ______ 19 ▢

20 If E is 4, F is 6, G is 8 and H is 2, answer this calculation.
(G + E) × H ÷ F = H × ▢ ______ 20 ▢

Q. 21–25 missing letters

The same **two** letters end the first word and begin the next word. Write the letters.

Example T R A I L I L L N E S S

21	P E A __ __	__ __ A R M	P I N __ __	__ __ O R E	21 ▢
22	R O B __ __	__ __ V E N T	C A B __ __	__ __ S I D E	22 ▢
23	C H A T __ __	__ __ R A N T	P O T __ __	__ __ P I N G	23 ▢
24	D U S T __ __	__ __ M I N E	P A L __ __	__ __ R A N D	24 ▢
25	A M P __ __	__ __ A G U E	C O U P __ __	__ __ A N	25 ▢

Q. 26–30 change a word

One word is incorrect in each sentence. Underline this word. Write the correct word on the line.

Example Climbing over that wall is not aloud. allowed

26 Some caramels have two humps. ______ 26 ▢

27 Dad went to the tailor to get a new suite. ______ 27 ▢

28 When a husband dies his wife becomes a window. ______ 28 ▢

29 The hunted house looked scary in the moonlight. ______ 29 ▢

30 When he is 19 he hopes to go to collage. ______ 30 ▢

MARK ▢

Q. 31–35

interpreting graphs

This bar chart shows the number of children attending the local primary school. Answer the questions.

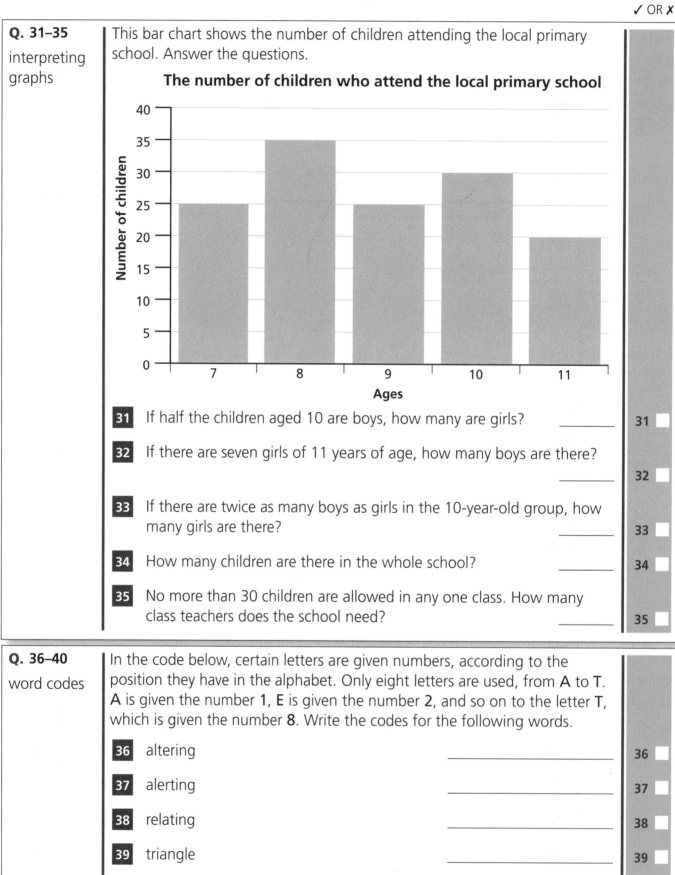

The number of children who attend the local primary school

Number of children (y-axis: 0, 5, 10, 15, 20, 25, 30, 35, 40)

Ages (x-axis: 7, 8, 9, 10, 11)

31 If half the children aged 10 are boys, how many are girls? _____   31 ☐

32 If there are seven girls of 11 years of age, how many boys are there?

_____   32 ☐

33 If there are twice as many boys as girls in the 10-year-old group, how many girls are there? _____   33 ☐

34 How many children are there in the whole school? _____   34 ☐

35 No more than 30 children are allowed in any one class. How many class teachers does the school need? _____   35 ☐

Q. 36–40

word codes

In the code below, certain letters are given numbers, according to the position they have in the alphabet. Only eight letters are used, from **A** to **T**. **A** is given the number **1**, **E** is given the number **2**, and so on to the letter **T**, which is given the number **8**. Write the codes for the following words.

36 altering _____   36 ☐

37 alerting _____   37 ☐

38 relating _____   38 ☐

39 triangle _____   39 ☐

40 integral _____   40 ☐

MARK ☐

MARK
✓ OR ✗

Q. 41–45
word meanings

Each of these words can have **two** meanings. Write the numbers of the two meanings in the table below.

Example		**41**		**42**		**43**		**44**		**45**	
organ		sharp		throw		rest		blue		plot	
11	12										

Meanings **1** what you do with a ball **2** to have a break **3** miserable **4** pointed **5** remainder **6** a colour **7** a cover for a bed **8** a piece of ground **9** tangy **10** to scheme and plan **11** a musical instrument **12** part of the body

41 ☐
42 ☐
43 ☐
44 ☐
45 ☐

Q. 46–50
letter codes

Answer these letter analogies. Use the alphabet to help you.

A B C D E F G H I J K L M N O P Q R S T U V W X Y Z

Example A is to B as C is to ___D___.

46 A is to Z as F is to _____.

47 CD is to WX as GH is to _____.

48 AV is to BW as CX is to _____.

49 ZW is to XU as VS is to _____.

50 LT is to MR as NP is to _____.

46 ☐
47 ☐
48 ☐
49 ☐
50 ☐

Q. 51–55
mixed-up groups

Two groups of three words have been mixed up in each question. Work out which would be the **middle** word in each group if they were in the correct order. Underline these **two** words.

Example city <u>adolescent</u> village <u>town</u> infant adult

51 officer monthly sergeant weekly daily private

52 train bus wind breeze taxi hurricane

53 jug cup brick building mug wall

54 multitude twentieth individual first tenth group

55 van lorry decade juggernaut century year

51 ☐
52 ☐
53 ☐
54 ☐
55 ☐

MARK ☐

MARK
✓ OR ✗

Q. 56–60

spot the
word

A four-letter word is hidden in each of these sentences. You will find
the hidden word at the end of one word and the beginning of the next.
Underline the hidden word and then write it on the line.

Example Daniel <u>end</u>ed his speech with a joke.   <u>lend</u>

56 They used to sell toffees and all kinds of sweets.   _____ | 56 ☐

57 To succeed you must have faith in your own abilities.   _____ | 57 ☐

58 The smugglers could not see the shore in the darkness.   _____ | 58 ☐

59 I gave the van door a slam but it would not shut properly. _____ | 59 ☐

60 Give the picture to your brother to look at.   _____ | 60 ☐

Q. 61–65

antonyms

Underline two words, **one** from each set of brackets, that have the **opposite**
meaning.

Example (<u>happy</u> kind mouth grin)   (smile <u>sad</u> face cheerful)

61 (interior inside ulterior downside)   (broadside exterior out excise) | 61 ☐

62 (some majority many lots)   (crowd throng multitude minority) | 62 ☐

63 (rich money miser greedy)   (spendthrift cash fortune millionaire) | 63 ☐

64 (imaginary ghost invisible genuine)   (present reality real past) | 64 ☐

65 (low deep height tall)   (depth altitude down basement) | 65 ☐

Q. 66–70

crosswords

Read the clues. Write the answers in the grid.

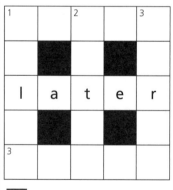

66 1 across   another word for yell | 66 ☐
67 3 across   bedding for animals | 67 ☐
68 1 down   parts of your shoes | 68 ☐
69 2 down   a water mammal | 69 ☐
70 3 down   to hurl or sling | 70 ☐

MARK ☐

MARK
✓ OR ✗

Q. 71–75

word categories

Below this table are 15 words. Write each word in the correct column.

71 vehicles	72 boats	73 sports	74 cooking	75 musical instruments

diving   whisk   cello   spatula   javelin   tricycle   kayak   trombone
oboe   junk   tandem   microwave   tractor   volleyball   barge

71 ☐
72 ☐
73 ☐
74 ☐
75 ☐

Q. 76–80

make a word

Look at how the second word is made from the first word in each pair.
Complete the third pair in the same way. Write the answers on the lines.

Example (fright rights)   (flight lights)   (height __eights__)

76 (gulps plugs)   (laps pals)   (parts _____)   76 ☐

77 (beauty beautiful)   (duty dutiful)   (plenty _____)   77 ☐

78 (light bright)   (liar briar)   (leather _____)   78 ☐

79 (bible title)   (barber tarter)   (bribe _____)   79 ☐

80 (rifle flier)   (fibre brief)   (hales _____)   80 ☐

Q. 81–85

word connections

Underline the **one** word that fits with **both** pairs of words in brackets.

Example (heart club) (ruby emerald)   jewel brain diamond card brooch

81 (type sort) (gentle loving)   empty kind soft letter adoring   81 ☐

82 (stare observe) (appearance impression)   demand look clean idea   82 ☐

83 (stone boulder) (sway tip)   dump diamond pebble lean rock   83 ☐

84 (encircle enclose) (jewellery band)   globe capture pendant ring sound   84 ☐

85 (feel discern) (sight taste)   sense hearing imagine speak appreciate   85 ☐

MARK ☐

MARK
✓ OR ✗

Q. 86–90

true statements

Read the information in each question. Circle the **only** statement (A, B, C, D or E) that has to be true, based on this information.

86 The Manx cat comes from the Isle of Man, which is an island between England and Ireland. It is an unusual cat because it has no tail.

A The Manx cat is half English and half Irish.
B All cats have tails.
C The Manx cat is unusual.
D All cats on the Isle of Man are without tails.

86 ☐

87 The Romans occupied Britain for about 400 years. They built a network of roads which were always as straight as possible. We still follow the course of a lot of them today.

A The Romans occupied Britain 400 years ago.
B Every road was completely straight.
C The roads are still used.
D The Romans occupied Britain for about four centuries.

87 ☐

88 The Worth Valley in West Yorkshire is home to a preserved and fully operational railway line some four miles long. It goes through Haworth, the nineteenth century home of the Brontë family. The three Brontë sisters wrote novels which are very famous.

A The Brontë sisters use the railway today.
B Before the railway was built, the sisters walked four miles to work.
C The railway line is still working in the twenty-first century.
D The Brontë sisters had a brother.

88 ☐

89 Luke is six years older than Flo. Flo is four years younger than Oscar, who is 18 next year.

A Luke is 19.
B Flo is four years of age.
C Luke and Flo are related.
D Oscar is older than Luke.

89 ☐

90 A mnemonic is a means of helping you to remember things. 'Richard of York gave battle in vain' is a mnemonic. It helps you to remember the colours of the rainbow in the correct order: red, orange, yellow, green, blue, indigo and violet.

A Richard of York was a mnemonic.
B Richard wore clothes of many colours.
C Indigo is a pale pink colour.
D A rainbow has seven colours.

90 ☐

MARK ☐

MARK
✓ OR ✗

Q. 91–95 jumbled words with clues	Each question has a word in CAPITALS. The letters in this word have been mixed up. Use the clue to work out what the word is. Write it on the line. **Example** NIBOR (a bird) __ROBIN__		
	91 CWITE (double)	_____	91 ☐
	92 PAEELHTN (a big animal)	_____	92 ☐
	93 CHUNL (a meal)	_____	93 ☐
	94 GARDEN (peril)	_____	94 ☐
	95 DUNANDREST (to grasp something)	_____	95 ☐

Q. 96–100 missing three-letter words	In each of these sentences, the word in CAPITALS has three letters missing. These three letters make a real three-letter word. Write the three-letter word on the line. **Example** My father SED me a photo of my mother. __HOW__		
	96 The doctor told the nurse to send in the next PANT.	_____	96 ☐
	97 At the funeral the mourners GARED round the grave.	_____	97 ☐
	98 The fans SHED to encourage their team.	_____	98 ☐
	99 Too many cooks spoil the BH.	_____	99 ☐
	100 The lesson will be STING in a few minutes.	_____	100 ☐

MARK ☐

END OF TEST

PROGRESS PAPER 12 TOTAL ☐

Topics chart

Schofield & Sims • Progress Papers • Verbal Reasoning 2

TOPICS COVERED		Paper	1	2	3	4	5	6	7	8	9	10	11	12	13	14	15	16	17	18
			Book 1						Book 2						Book 3					
vocabulary		analogies	•	•		•	•	•	•	•	•	•	•		•		•			•
		antonyms	•	•		•		•			•	•	•	•	•	•	•	•	•	•
		complete the sentence	•		•	•	•			•	•		•		•				•	
		compound words							•	•				•				•		•
		crosswords				•			•										•	
		mixed-up groups	•		•		•			•	•	•			•	•		•		•
		odd ones out	•	•	•				•			•	•	•					•	
		rhyming words										•			•		•			
		synonyms				•	•		•	•	•		•		•	•	•			•
		word categories		•	•		•	•	•	•	•	•	•	•	•			•		•
		word connections		•	•	•	•	•	•	•	•	•	•	•	•			•		
		word meanings		•	•				•		•	•		•	•		•	•	•	
spelling		add a letter			•	•	•	•		•			•			•		•		•
		change a letter														•		•		
		change a word			•			•						•		•		•	•	
		join two words to make one	•	•	•		•	•			•	•	•	•	•			•		•
		jumbled words in grids		•	•	•		•		•					•	•	•	•		•
		jumbled words in sentences		•	•		•					•			•				•	•
		jumbled words with clues	•	•							•			•						
		leftover letters				•			•											
		missing four-letter words															•		•	
		missing letters	•	•	•	•	•		•	•		•		•			•	•	•	•
		missing three-letter words			•	•	•		•			•		•	•			•	•	
		move a letter						•		•			•							•

TOPICS COVERED

Category	Topic	Book 1 Paper 1	2	3	4	5	6	Book 2 Paper 7	8	9	10	11	12	Book 3 Paper 13	14	15	16	17	18
spelling (continued)	spot the word	•	•	•	•	•	•	•	•	•	•	•	•	•	•	•		•	•
	take a letter										•								
	which word		•		•	•		•	•	•						•	•	•	•
	word chains		•	•	•		•	•		•	•	•		•		•	•	•	•
logical reasoning	always has	•				•		•								•			
	mixed-up sentences	•	•	•	•		•	•		•						•			
	mixed-up questions		•	•			•								•				
	position problems	•					•		•									•	
	sorting information		•		•					•	•	•		•					•
	time problems		•	•				•		•	•	•		•				•	
	true statements	•				•							•				•	•	
	word grids	•	•					•		•		•		•	•	•			
codes, sequences and patterns	alphabetical order	•		•	•	•			•	•	•		•		•				
	letter codes	•											•						
	letter sequences		•		•		•	•	•	•	•	•	•	•	•		•	•	
	make a word		•		•			•			•						•		
	match the codes		•		•				•		•								
	number sequences				•		•	•	•	•		•	•		•	•		•	
	symbol codes	•			•		•	•	•	•					•	•			
	word codes			•								•			•		•		•
numerical reasoning	algebra						•												
	interpreting graphs		•		•	•	•			•		•	•	•	•	•			
	interpreting tables	•										•					•		
	letters for numbers	•		•		•		•	•			•	•	•	•	•		•	•
	number connections	•										•							

Progress chart

Write the score (out of 100) for each paper in the box provided at the bottom of the chart. Then colour in the column above the box to the appropriate height to represent this score.

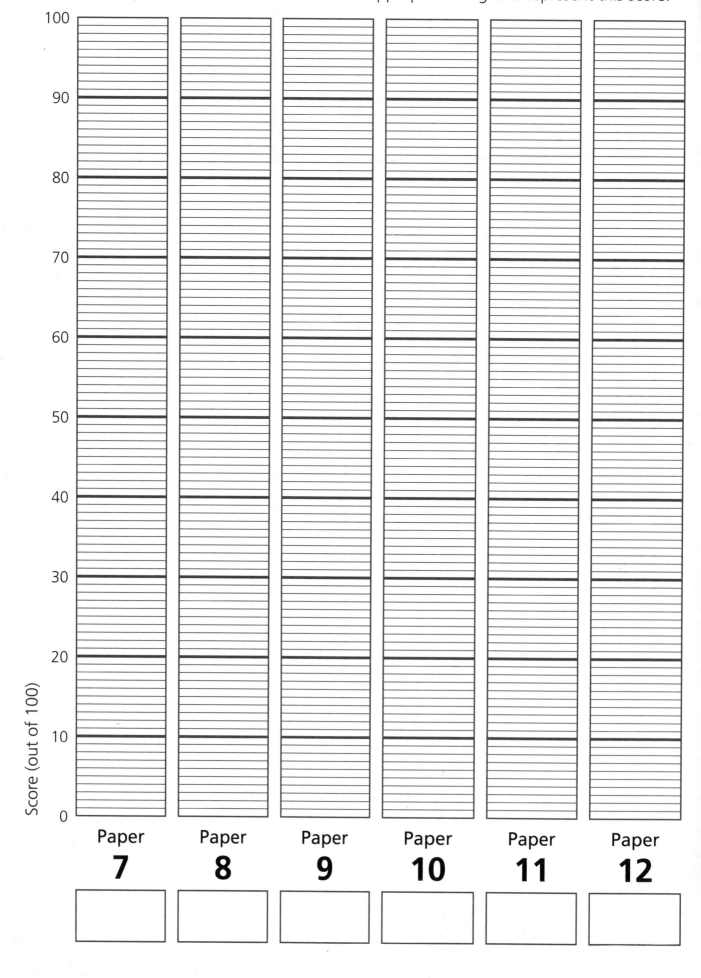